CLAUDIO MONT

CHRISTMAS VESPERS

Antiphons, psalms and hymn
for soloists, double choir,
instruments and
organ continuo

edited by

DENIS STEVENS

NOVELLO PUBLISHING LIMITED

Order No: NOV 070430

Second edition (with corrections) 1996

Changes from the First edition are indicated in the score by an asterisk (*).

The Editor has also noted:

Metrical relationships: p. 1, 2, 30, 36. 37. 56, 57, 58, 62, 63, 73, 76, 78, 108, 109, 111. For a less resonant building, the proportion could be changed to dotted minim = minim (or vice-versa).

Copies of the First edition should be amended accordingly.

CONTENTS

1   Dixit Dominus   page   1

2   Confitebor tibi Domine   41

3   Beatus vir   56

4   Laudate pueri   79

5   Laudate Dominum   98

6   Christe Redemptor omnium (Hymn)   113

    Commentary   117

DURATION ABOUT 43 MINUTES

The *Magnificat* (duration about 17 minutes)
which brings the Vespers to a close is published
by Novello in an edition by Denis Stevens and
John Steele.

PREFACE

I⊤ has recently been shown, in a revealing study of early music on records (1952-1977), that Monteverdi ranks an easy first in an impressive list of great composers, and that his *Vespers of 1610* have been more frequently recorded than any other major work by any composer prior to 1650.[1] Yet however encouraging this may be (and even though quantity does not necessarily guarantee quality), there is one important question that scholars and performers should have asked themselves time and time again: if Monteverdi devoted a not inconsiderable part of the last fifty years of his life to the composition of large-scale works for the liturgy — a fact borne out by documentary as well as musical evidence — why do we not hear about it, and why do we not hear those works?

The problem and its solution

Where, indeed, are all the other settings of Vespers? He may have been in his early thirties when he first experimented with the form, admittedly on a small scale, for he and a quintet of musicians accompanied Vincenzo Gonzaga, Fourth Duke of Mantua, on a military expedition against the Turks in 1595. Under campaign conditions, allied dignitaries were invited to the Gonzaga headquarters for a banquet followed by solemn Vespers, which (according to Maria Bellonci) were 'sung by the Italian musicians under the direction of Claudio Monteverdi. Almost certainly the music was composed by him. How pleasant it would be to track it down and follow the lofty emotion of the great musician who was the only immortal there among so many princes, archdukes and generals; the man who, on the eve of battle and under the Hungarian sky, made the sublime decision to transport his listeners into a civilized world of his own where the element of the eternal is fixed for ever in pure sound.'[2]

Of those 'Vespers in Time of War', no trace remains. But the set he composed and published fifteen years after that campaign not only survived — it reappears even now in one new edition after another. Less notice has been taken of the psalms, hymns, and Magnificats in the *Selva morale e spirituale* of 1640, also of the psalms in the posthumously published collection of 1650 to which Cavalli made a contribution;[3] the reason for this lack of attention stems from a failure to group these apparently disparate and unrelated works into plausible liturgical entities. Attempts to record them *seriatim* have so far shed little light, and the available handful of editions for practical use cannot, by its very nature, provide a set of Vespers that would be in any way acceptable.

A solution to the problem was outlined in a little-known but pioneering article[4] by Monsignor Giuseppe Biella (1906-1967), a scholar, composer and conductor who directed

[1] Elizabeth Roche, 'Early Music on Records in the last 25 years — 1', *The Musical Times* CXX (January 1979) pp. 35-36.

[2] Maria Bellonci, *A Prince of Mantua: The Life and Times of Vincenzo Gonzaga* (London, 1956) p. 166. Although a historical novel, the book is based on authentic documents, this particular passage stemming from a diary written by Fortunato Cardi (Mantua, Archivio Gonzaga, busta 388).

[3] *Messa a quattro voci, et Salmi* (Vincenti). There is also a *Confitebor* a 4 in Sabino's anthology of Vesper psalms (1627), and a *Laudate pueri* in manuscript at Kassel briefly noted in *The Musical Times* CXVIII (July 1977) p. 580.

[4] Giuseppe Biella, 'I "Vespri dei Santi" di Claudio Monteverdi', *Musica Sacra* 90 (November 1966) pp. 144-153.

in Milan a composite *Vespere dei Santi* with his Polifonica Ambrosiana. It was he who pointed out that the *Selva* contains all of the required music for Vespers of Apostles and Evangelists, Martyrs, Confessor-Bishops, Doctors and Abbots, while the *Messa, Salmi, Letanie* of 1650 offers psalms for Vespers of the Blessed Virgin and for many of the saints. Carrying his theory a stage further, I suggested that the combined publications could be used to reconstruct Vespers for six major feasts from the *Temporale* (including Christmas), and seven more from the *Proprium de Sanctis*. [5]

At the same time I mentioned that the instrumental resources specified in the *Selva*, however haphazard they may at first appear, turn out to be clearly and logically organized when the psalms are placed in liturgical order: one set of Vespers needs a fair-sized ensemble of strings and brass supporting a virtuoso vocal ensemble, whereas the other calls for a more modest group of singers and players. [6] Since Christmas Vespers ranks as a major feast (Double of the First Class), the present edition combines works scored for a suitably opulent ensemble of seven soloists (SSATTBarB), double choir (SATB/SATB), strings, four trombones (TTTB), and organ.

I am quite sure that within a short time choir directors throughout the world will be busily putting together Vespers by Monteverdi for all manner of feasts within the scope of the church year. Let them not, however, expect to include ordinary Sundays or Easter, for which *In exitu Israel* is the final psalm, nor Corpus Christi which requires *Beati omnes*. There is no extant setting of either psalm by the divine Claudio.

The background

Sceptics may well ask why this kind of reconstruction is necessary, when there is nothing inherently wrong in performing an isolated hymn, psalm, or Magnificat in a miscellaneous concert programme. By the same token it is perfectly acceptable to perform a Gloria, Credo, Sanctus or Agnus Dei from heterogeneous collections originating in some medieval scriptorium. On the other hand, the recognition of paired Mass sections based on the same *cantus firmus* or linked by mode, style and technique often results in a far more impressive tonal edifice — a work whose memorable amplitude and heavenly lengths fit well with the sense of space imparted by a high-vaulted chapel or cathedral. There is no doubt that the average choirmaster of the late middle ages knew how to put together a polyphonic Mass from individual movements in the great manuscript collections at Aosta, Bologna, Modena, Trent and elsewhere, [7] or (more strictly speaking) from their workaday originals long since destroyed; and as for Vespers, he would perform a similar task with the antiphons and psalms of a choirbook such as Verona, Biblioteca Capitolare 759, where the absence of *cantus firmus* and the disregard for strict application of tone or mode allowed the maximum of choice and flexibility. [8]

The typical *maestro di cappella* of the renaissance and early baroque followed those same traditional guide-lines, working now from printed editions whose *fons et origo* was the classic collection of Adrian Willaert and Jachet of Mantua — *I salmi appertinenti alli vesperi per tutte le feste dell'anno* — published by Gardane in 1550. A fundamental and thorough-going study of this vast repertory by Jeffrey G. Kurtzman [9] reveals not only the

[5] Denis Stevens, *Monteverdi: Sacred, Secular, and Occasional Music* (London, 1978) p. 82ff.

[6] Stevens, *op. cit.* p. 84.

[7] The most complete English source for music of this period is the Old Hall Manuscript, now British Library Add. MS 57950.

[8] Masakata Kanazawa, 'Two Vesper repertories from Verona, *c.* 1500', *Rivista italiana di musicologia* X (1975) p. 171.

[9] Jeffrey G. Kurtzman, 'Some Historical Perspectives on the Monteverdi Vespers', *Analecta musicologica* 15 (1975) pp. 29-86.

variety but also the extreme subtlety of Vesper publications in Italy, where conditions for performance ranged from the rough-and-ready vocal quintet to the elaborate choral and instrumental establishments found in the chapels of princes. As in Monteverdi's various sets of material for Vesper services, the psalms are sometimes appropriate to the Blessed Virgin and to feasts of virgins, sometimes to major feasts of the church year and to the *Sanctorale* in general. A few publications combine both types and thereby offer the choir director a wide choice both in liturgical needs and in vocal and instrumental scoring.

For the present reconstruction, I have chosen Christmas Vespers because of their outstanding appeal and importance throughout the ages. An Englishman who visited Venice towards the end of the 16th century wrote that 'the Duke [i.e. Doge] with the Senate makes some 22 publicke Walkes without Triumph to the Church of St Marke, whereof that upon Christmas Eve is the most solemn, when the Vesper is sung with the most exquisite musicke both of Instruments and voyces'.[10] It is clear, too, from the composer's correspondence that he looked upon his work leading up to the Christmas season as by far the most demanding of the entire year.

In a letter to Alessandro Striggio dated 29 December 1616, he claims to have taken a month to write and copy out a Mass for Christmas Eve, and in another letter, this time from Parma to the Marquis Enzo Bentivoglio (30 October 1627) he asks for leave to return to Venice in order to fulfil these special duties.[11] He was in Parma again in November of the following year, when the Procurators begged him to return as soon as possible, for such a solemn feast could not be properly celebrated without his presence.[12] When time permitted, he would compose a Mass and Vespers for one or other of the Venetian confraternities, and be well rewarded for his pains.[13]

Performance practice

The general goal should be quadraphonic, or more, rather than merely stereophonic. A separate *schola* for the plainsong antiphons should sing from a gallery or distant chapel. The double-choir compositions (*Dixit Dominus* and *Magnificat*) should of course be performed with maximum separation compatible with good ensemble. Soloists can form a separate unit with their own continuo: a small organ ought to be sufficient, but a bass lute and viola da gamba or violone can be added if available. The strings and trombones, together with their organ continuo, may serve to separate the two main choirs, and it should be borne in mind that since the trombones double the voices on an *ad hoc* basis, they need not be divided in any way. If, as they should be, the antiphons are doubled (that is, sung both before and after the psalms and Magnificat), this will allow more time for soloists to move as unobtrusively as possible and to be ready for the next item.

In the year 1612, just before Monteverdi arrived in Venice to take up his position as director of music at St Mark's, at least three composers published collections of church music prefaced by hints on performance. It is unfortunate in some ways that Lodovico Grossi da Viadana is known solely for his *Cento concerti ecclesiastici* of 1602, for his *Salmi à 4 Chori per cantare e concertare* (Vincenti, 1612) offer advice to the conductor in the form of a preface whose brevity and simplicity belie its true importance. Although Viadana is speaking mainly of *cori spezzati* accompanied only by organ (and possibly chitarrone) according to the printed part-books, his advice on the number and strength of each vocal

[10] Fynes Morison, *Itinerary* (1617), edited by C. Hughes as *Shakespeare's Europe* (London, 1903) p. 144ff.

[11] Denis Stevens, *The Letters of Claudio Monteverdi* (London, 1980) Nos. 22 and 113. For other information about Vespers, see Nos. 11, 29 and 125.

[12] Denis Arnold, *Monteverdi* (London, 1963) p. 203.

[13] Letter dated 13 March 1620 (No. 49 in edition cited above).

line—not to mention the suggestions for instrumental doubling by wind, brass, and stringed instruments—is tantamount to an early treatise on instrumentation, albeit in miniature.[14] Two lesser-known composers, Fergusio and Donati, discuss the theory and practice of separated choirs and 'distant singing' in their anthologies of dialogues and motets, without however going into such detail as Viadana does.[15]

Continuo

If more than one organ can be pressed (or blown) into service, so much the better: portative and positive organs clearly played their part in baroque continuo practice, but it is worth while remembering the advice of Viadana who exhorts the player accompanying the soloists to regulate timbre and dynamics with the utmost care, and to indulge in no ornamentation whatever. In the present edition, the original bass is shown as the lowest part in the bass stave, whether stems are up or down, the realization being editorial. When the continuo part is marked SOLO, the bass line should be doubled by a solo cello: all cellos and basses play in the sections marked TUTTI.

Violas

An editorial viola line has been provided for *Dixit Dominus*, *Beatus vir* and *Laudate Dominum* to add sonority and to give the players something to do rather than remain silent. Purists may omit these lines, though they will notice that I have based them largely on the extant vocal parts, a method used by the composer himself in the *Magnificat*.

Trombones

These are mentioned by name in the titles of *Dixit Dominus*, *Laudate Dominum* and *Magnificat*. In general, they double vocal lines in such a way that the quartet will play as many complete chords as possible for fullness of sound and the best possible spacing.

Ornamentation

Successful and convincing vocal ornamentation depends absolutely upon an intelligent development and deployment of both technique and good taste: either one deprived of the other may lead to disaster. Notes printed small show suggested embellishment, which (as will be seen) I have not used to excess. The actual passages are based on treatises by Giovanni Bassano, Vincenzo Bonizzi, G. B. Bovicelli, Antonio Brunelli, Girolamo dalla Casa, Giovanni Luca Conforto, Francesco Rognoni, and G. B. Spadi. Singers interested in improving their technique should study, in particular, the Foreword to Caccini's *Le nuove musiche*,[16] and the 'Advice to the Reader' in Brunelli's *Varii esercitii . . . per una, e due voci* (Pignoni, Florence).[17]

---

[14] A facsimile of the original and a German translation are given in Paul Winter, *Der mehrchörige Stil* (Frankfurt, 1964) pp. 94, 43.

[15] Denis Arnold, 'Monteverdi's Church Music: Some Venetian Traits', *The Monthly Musical Record* 88 (May 1958) p. 87.

[16] Oliver Strunk, *Source Readings in Music History* (London, 1950) pp. 377-392; H. Wiley Hitchcock, *Le nuove musiche* (Madison, 1970) pp. 43-56.

[17] Claudio Sartori, *Bibliografia della musica strumentale italiana* (Florence, 1952) p. 202.

Time-signatures

More than forty shifts from duple to triple time occur in the five psalms alone, and since the sections in *proportio tripla* are notated in various ways — $\mathbf{\phi}\,{}^{3}_{1}$, $\mathbf{\phi}\,{}^{3}_{2}$, $\mathbf{\phi}3$ — the strictness of metrical and mathematical relationships as they were understood in the 15th century should not be allowed to inhibit the freedom of interpretation which is known to have existed in Monteverdi's time. Note-values in the *tripla* sections have been quartered throughout, with the one exception of the hymn *Christe Redemptor omnium*, where a $\frac{3}{2}$ time-signature seems more suitable than $\frac{3}{4}$ as a vehicle for a calm and unhurried tempo.

In the final analysis, much depends upon the acoustic of the hall or church in which the work is performed. Having conducted choral-orchestral music in many abbeys and cathedrals, above all in St Mark's, Venice, where Monteverdi himself had to face problems of ensemble and balance, I would urge the adoption of a fairly flexible attitude towards metrical relationships, and readiness (even as late as the final rehearsal) for subtle adjustments that will help the music to make its fullest impact. To give but one example of this kind of adjustment, there is the transition at bars 262-266 in *Dixit Dominus*, where it seems advisable — as in many comparable passages in Monteverdi's sacred and secular music [18] — to standardize the length of an up-beat pattern, in this case linked with the word 'et'. But in certain acoustics it may prove advantageous to think of the 'Sicut erat' as a steady $\frac{2}{2}$ with minim becoming equivalent to dotted minim at the change of time. In many other situations it will be found expedient to maintain the same crotchet beat through a temporary metrical shift.

Accidentals

Enclosure within square brackets distinguishes accidentals that have been added by way of editorial suggestion; others not present in the original text — i.e. those supplied for precautionary reasons or consequent on the modernization of notation — are printed in small size. The treble stave of the continuo constitutes an exception to the foregoing: all accidentals before notes played by the right hand are given in normal rather than small size, as an aid to legibility, the entire stave being in any case editorially supplied.

Antiphons

The antiphons and the five psalms are those proper to First Vespers; but in view of the thematic link between the 'Alleluia' at the close of the antiphon to Magnificat at Second Vespers and the opening notes of Monteverdi's double-choir *Magnificat*, [19] I have chosen *Hodie Christus natus est* to preface this most sumptuous of his settings of the canticle. [20] A complete service for Second Vespers would be an impossibility since there is no surviving setting by Monteverdi of the fourth psalm, *De profundis*. For those who prefer an unadulterated sequence of texts for First Vespers, the Magnificat antiphon *Cum ortus fuerit* is given as an alternative to *Hodie*. Both antiphons are transposed up a tone to agree with the higher pitch of the *Magnificat*. Otherwise, no changes have been made, and it will be found that the five antiphons connect smoothly with the tonality of the psalms,

---

[18] Wolfgang Osthoff, *Das dramatische Spätwerk Claudio Monteverdis* (Munich, 1960) pp. 211-214.

[19] Edited by Denis Stevens and John Steele (Novello, London).

[20] It is worthy of note that Monteverdi set *Hodie* as a motet a 3 in his youthful *Sacrae cantiunculae* of 1582. I do not recommend its use in this context in view of the great disparity of style and technique between the two publications.

In accordance with tradition, Monteverdi sets alternate verses in polyphony, and this procedure has been followed here with the proper chant for verses 1, 3, 5 and 7. Although his original designations for the solo vocal parts are A T B the ranges suggest T T Bar, which can be varied if desired by S S A in one or more verses.

Acknowledgments

I wish to thank Sir William Glock, under whose enlightened regime at the BBC I was able to introduce the greater part of the *Christmas Vespers* at a Promenade Concert in the Royal Albert Hall on 18 August 1970. My sincere gratitude extends also to the Accademia Monteverdiana, Professor Jeffrey Kurtzman, Professor Pierre Tagmann, Mr Desmond Ratcliffe, and to my wife Leocadia for her constant encouragement and help.

Santa Barbara, California   DENIS STEVENS
1979

INSTRUMENTATION

3 Tenor Trombones
Bass Trombone

Strings*

Organ

*Violas supplied editorially; see the Preface.

Trombone and string parts for this volume
and for the *Magnificat* are available on hire.

which are not based on any particular tones with the exception of three brief appearances of Tone 8G in the opening section of *Dixit Dominus*. This loosely bound association of antiphon and psalm goes back to the 15th century, when (just as in the Verona manuscript mentioned earlier) psalm tones corresponded with the modes of antiphons only in very rare instances. [21]

Psalms

Dixit Dominus has not generally been recognized as a double-choir composition because the parts marked 'secondo choro' in the *Selva morale* are in a confused state, like so much else in this collection. [22] But a reworking of this psalm appears, quite clearly for divided choirs (though without violins), in the *Messa, Salmi, Letanie* of 1650 where it has lain unperceived for several centuries due to the completely different opening section. When the 8-part tutti at 'Virgam virtutis' is reached, the correspondence becomes obvious, and from this point onwards similar and dissimilar sections alternate.

Confitebor tibi Domine offers a fascinating possibility for different types of performance: either fully choral, or (as the composer tells us) for soprano solo accompanied by strings. My version combines both by allocating alternate psalm verses to soloist and chorus. The composer's partiality for different versions of this text has been noted elsewhere, [23] as too his borrowing of themes from secular works written much earlier. [24]

Beatus vir is the only psalm taken from the collection of 1650. Like *Dixit Dominus*, its divided choir structure has gone unnoticed, the more so in this case because the forces are beguilingly uneven, with a semichorus (SA) contrasting with a five-part choir and soloists. It would, of course, be possible to replace the semichorus by two soloists able to hold their own against the combined tutti, but this is a matter for individual choice.

Laudate pueri is mainly for soloists: their declamation and observance of hemiola (bars 111-113) and correct accentuation of text (bars 165-180) is of paramount importance. The brief tutti sections could be sung by semichorus.

Laudate Dominum, printed in a somewhat muddled condition in the *Selva morale*, has here been divested of superfluous voice-parts — they were duplicates of tutti sections — and supplied with the violas and trombones suggested by the composer.

Hymn

At the end of the *Deus tuorum militum* a 3 in the *Selva morale* is a note to the effect that the same music can serve for other hymns in the same metre, such as *Jesu corona virginum* and *Christe Redemptor omnium*. This shows that in spite of the introduction of a variant text in the revised Roman Breviary of 1632 (*Jesu Redemptor omnium*, still in use until recently), the Venetians retained the original text of the pseudo-Ambrosian hymn. Perhaps the best-known translation is that of J. M. Neale (*The English Hymnal*, No. 17).

[21] Tom R. Ward, 'The Polyphonic Office Hymn and the Liturgy of Fifteenth Century Italy', *Musica disciplina* XXVI (1972) p. 176.

[22] In dedicating the *Selva morale* to Eleonora Gonzaga, widow of the Emperor Ferdinand II, Monteverdi admitted that the publication was not as perfect as he would have wished it to be. For further details, see Denis Stevens, 'Claudio Monteverdi: *Selva morale e spirituale*', in *Claudio Monteverdi e il suo tempo* (Verona, 1969) pp. 423-434; Denis Arnold, 'Formal design in Monteverdi's church music', *op.cit.* pp. 187-216; Arnold, 'A Background Note on Monteverdi's Hymn Settings', in *Scritti in onore di Luigi Ronga* (Verona, 1973) pp. 33-44.

[23] Jerome Roche, 'Monteverdi — An Interesting Example of Second Thoughts', *The Music Review* 32 (1971) pp. 193-204.

[24] Denis Stevens, 'Madrigali Guerrieri, et Amorosi', *The Musical Quarterly* LIII (1967) p. 182ff.

CHRISTMAS VESPERS

Edited by Denis Stevens

CLAUDIO MONTEVERDI

1 DIXIT DOMINUS (Psalm 109)*

* Authorized version Psalm 110

20240

28

20240

2 CONFITEBOR TIBI (Psalm 110)*

* Authorized version Psalm 111

† notated in G clef

46

i - ni - ti - um sa - pi - en - ti - ae ti - mor Do - mi - ni.

i - ni - ti - um sa - pi - en - ti - ae ti - mor Do - mi - ni.

i - ni - ti - um sa - pi - en - ti - ae ti - mor Do - mi - ni.

i - ni - ti - um sa - pi - en - ti - ae ti - mor Do - mi - ni.

In-tel-le - ctus_ bo-nus o - mni - bus fa-ci-en - ti-bus e -

In-tel-le - ctus bo-nus o-mni - bus fa-ci-en - ti-bus e -

In-tel-le - ctus bo-nus o-mni - bus fa-ci-en - ti-bus e -

In-tel-le - ctus bo-nus o-mni - bus fa-ci-en - ti-bus e -

In-tel-le - ctus bo-nus o-mni - bus fa-ci-en - ti-bus e -

130

_ Spi-ri-tu-i San - cto. Si-cut e-rat in_ prin - ci - pi - o, et nunc,_ et

135

sem - per, _ nunc et sem-per, et_ in_ sae - cu - la sae - cu - lo - rum.

140
TUTTI

A - men. Si-cut e-rat in_ prin - ci - pi - o, et nunc,_ et

S II

Si-cut e-rat in prin - ci - pi-o, et nunc, et

A

Si-cut e-rat in prin - ci - pi- o, et nunc, et

T

Si-cut e-rat in_ prin - ci - pi - o, et nunc, et

B

140
TUTTI

3 BEATUS VIR (Psalm 111)*

*Authorized version Psalm 112

62

20240

SEMICHORUS

4 LAUDATE PUERI (Psalm 112)*

* Authorized version Psalm 113

94

5 LAUDATE DOMINUM (Psalm 116)*

100

20240

104

20240

et in sae - cu - la   sae-cu - lo - rum.   A - men.

6 CHRISTE REDEMPTOR OMNIUM (HYMN)

Soloists sing *Amen* (page 115) after verse 7

*Alternatively Baritone or Bass

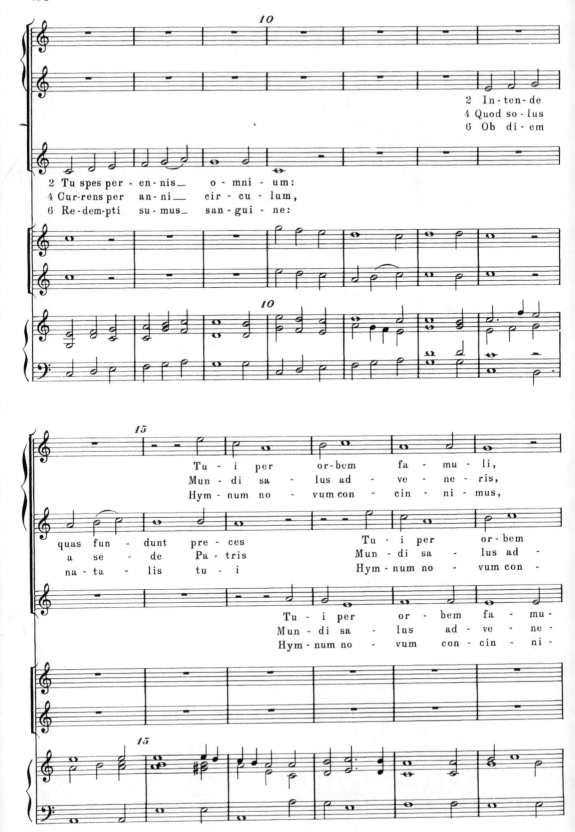

TENOR

Ho-di - e Chris - tus na-tus_ est: ho-di - e

Sal-va-tor ap - pa-ru - it: ho-di - e in ter-ra_ ca-nunt An-ge - li,

lae-tan - tur Arch-an-ge - li: ho-di - e_____ ex-sul - tant ju-sti,_

di-cen-tes:_ Glo - ri - a in ex-cel - sis De - o,_ al-le - lu - ia.

Here follows without pause the Monteverdi *Magnificat.*＊

[Alternate antiphon for First Vespers]

TENOR

Cum_ or - tus fu - e - rit sol de cae - lo,

vi - de - bi - tis Re - gem re - gum

pro - ce - den - tem _____ u _____ Pa - tre,

tam - quam spon - sum de thu - la - mo su - o.

＊Edited by Denis Stevens and John Steele (Novello, 1969)

COMMENTARY

The following comments refer to the original edition of the *Selva morale e spirituale*, unless qualified by '1650', which refers to the *Messa a quattro voci et Salmi* of that year. Minor errors of an obviously typographical nature have for the most part been silently corrected, and the length of final notes has been adjusted for the convenience of present-day performers. The use of pauses in the part-books of both collections shows considerable inconsistency, and again in the interest of performers I have standardized or added these wherever it seemed appropriate and helpful to do so.

Dixit Dominus

Bar	Part	
25	violin I	first quaver, A
30	alto I	quaver, D
46	basso continuo	crotchet, B
77	violin I	2nd and 3rd beats omitted
78	violin II	rest omitted
115	tenor I	minim, G (also 1650)
150	bass I, II	entries omitted in 1650
156	alto II	2nd F, dotted crotchet
162	alto II	E, D, crotchets
166	basso continuo	'a 2 tenori et 3 tromboni'
205	tenor I	2nd crotchet, A
253	tenor I, II	this section for 2 sopranos in 1650
261	tenor II	F, F, both sharp
272	basso continuo	sharp below D
279	alto II	1st crotchet F natural (also 1650)
280	alto II	both crotchets F natural (also 1650)
281	bass I, II	entries omitted in 1650
289	alto, tenor	entries omitted in 1650

Confitebor tibi Domine

73	soprano I, tenor	octaves probably intentional
102	soprano II	last crotchet, G
131	soprano I	a strict interpretation of original note-values in second half of bar results in consecutive sevenths between soprano and basso continuo; the suggested modification may reflect what was intended
132	soprano I	musical pun

Beatus vir

Bar	Part	
12	tenor I	G, F, crotchets (1650)
37	violin II	D, D, crotchets omitted (1650)
38	alto	last note, F natural (1650)
92	basso continuo	sharp below E (1650)
124	basso continuo	original mark 'piano' (1650)
129	tenor II	last crotchet, G (1650)
166	alto	semichorus: last two notes, A, A (1650)
220	violin II	F, E, omitted (1650)
237	alto	semichorus: octaves with tenor II probably intentional (1650)

Laudate pueri

111		beginning of bar extended by one crotchet in order to clarify following hemiola pattern (bars 111-133)
128	violin II	second note A (1650)
164		change of metre delayed to assist correct declamation (bars 165-181)
209	tenor II	last note, E

Laudate Dominum

15		rhythm in all parts adjusted to soprano and basso continuo
49-62		tenor parts exchanged
50	soprano II	F natural here (and in viola) by analogy with D minor chord at bar 30
78-107		tenor parts exchanged